How to Sp...

Nutty Tart

An essential Bubblegum™ guide

Ged Backland and Phil Renshaw

Nutty Tart

She's crazy and she's scatty

a real class apart

It's fair to say in every way

she's a grade 'A' nutty tart!

Nutty Tart

Nutty Tart is nuttier than a squirrel's supper. She is the craziest of the Bubblegum Crew. She bounces around having a truly nutty time. Wild, wacky and wonderful, she makes any gathering complete.

Most Likely to Say...

Have a 'narna!

Most Likely to Be...

Out to lunch

Fave Colour

Sea Green

Bestest Friends with...

Groovy Gal

Disco Diva

Slap Head

Ginger Nut just wishes
that Nutty Tart would stop
Shouting out across the street
"Aye up, Carrot Top!"

Diamond Geezer is a top bloke
and difficult to phase
But just five mins with Nutty Tart
sends him mad for days!

Hunny Bunny is very sweet
and is everybody's mate
Nutty Tart is nice to her
'cos she thinks Bunny's really great.

Designer Diva wears what's cool
her coolness doesn't stop
Nutty Tart looks just as fab
in clothes from a charity shop.

Disco Diva is straight on the floor
for an Abba tune or two
The same applies for Nutty Tart
but she loves 'Agadoo'!

Boy Racer will offer a lift
to anyone that's needy
Nutty Tart gets in the car
and makes him drive real speedy!

Diet Slave worries every day
'bout eating chips and stuff
Nutty Tart just doesn't care
she scoffs 'till she's had enough.

Cool Dude likes nothing better
than a coffee and a chill
Nutty Tart swoons over him
'cos she thinks he's really brill.

Nutty Moo is really crazy
but a big softie at heart
And she's got herself a loopy twin
in soppy Nutty Tart!

Choccy Fiend asks Nutty Tart
to a massive choccy fest
Nutty Tart quickly whizzes round
she thinks choccy is the best!

If anyone touches Slap Head's bonce
he'll have a bloomin blub
But Nutty Tart just can't resist
giving it a little rub!

tee
hee

100% Bad likes to look
moody, mean 'n' tuff
Nutty Tart wants to play fight
but Bad has had enough!

Shoe Queen once went shopping
with Nutty Tart for shoes
She ended up in wellies
and got the shopping blues!

Veggie just loves Nutty Tart
'cos she's flippin' mental
But when it comes to animals
she's very kind and gentle.

So there you have it, it's all very clear
The low-down on Nutty Tart is here.

If it all sounds familiar, if it rings true
Chances are, Nutty Tart's you!